I Can Learn

Get Ready for Reading

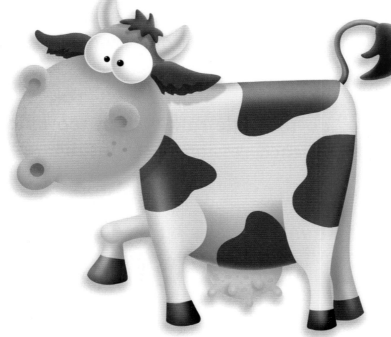

Written by Nicola Morgan

Illustrated by John Haslam

 This book belongs to

....

EGMONT

Tips for happy home learning

Make learning fun by working at your child's pace
and always giving tasks which s/he can do.
Tasks that are too difficult will discourage her/him
from trying again.

Give encouragement and praise and remember
to award gold stars and sticker badges for
effort as well as good work.

Always do too little rather than too much,
and finish each session on a positive note.

Don't work when you or your child
is tired or hungry.

Reinforce workbook activities and new ideas by
making use of real objects around the home.

EGMONT
We bring stories to life

Published in Great Britain by Egmont UK Limited,
239 Kensington High Street, London W8 6SA
This edition published 2008
© 2008 Egmont UK Limited
All rights reserved.
ISBN 978 1 4052 3991 2
1 3 5 7 9 10 8 6 4 2
Printed in Italy

Hello! I'm Curly Cat.

I'm going to help you learn to read. When we read we look at the words – not the pictures. Point to some words on this page.

Can you put a circle round just the words?

hat

flower

cat

house

tree

balloon

Draw a circle round the words again.
What do you think the words say?

house   sun   balloon   tree

hat   kite   mug   star

A special word is your name.
Ask a grown-up to help you write it here:

You have learnt about words.

Can you draw a picture of yourself?

You are doing such good work.

Make a pair!

Use your eyes carefully to find shapes which are the same and join them with a line.

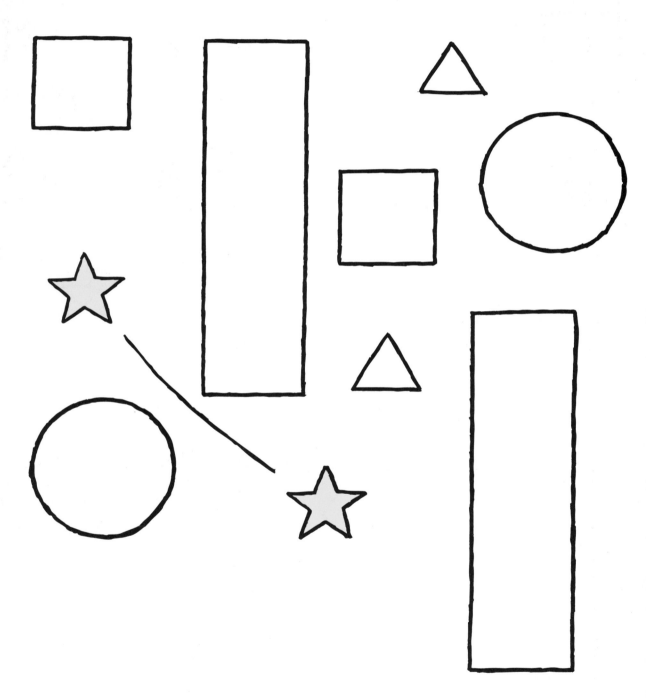

Note for parents: Identifying similarities is an important pre-reading skill. Ask your child to sort toy bricks that are similar in shape, colour or size.

Matching shapes

Let's do some more matching.

Note for parents: Children learn new skills more easily if you use real objects, such as toy bricks, cutlery etc. Practise matching skills with games such as lotto, snap and dominoes.

I need some help. These gloves are muddled up.
Can you find the ones which match and join them with
a line?

Use your eyes really carefully here.
Join the snowflakes which are the same.

Can you draw some snowflakes of your own?

Note for parents: Reward is a vital part of learning. The best reward is praise, but a sticker, means a lot to your child. Praise your child for trying, even if s/he needed help.

You will find these easy.
Look at the first one in each line
then circle one that's the same.

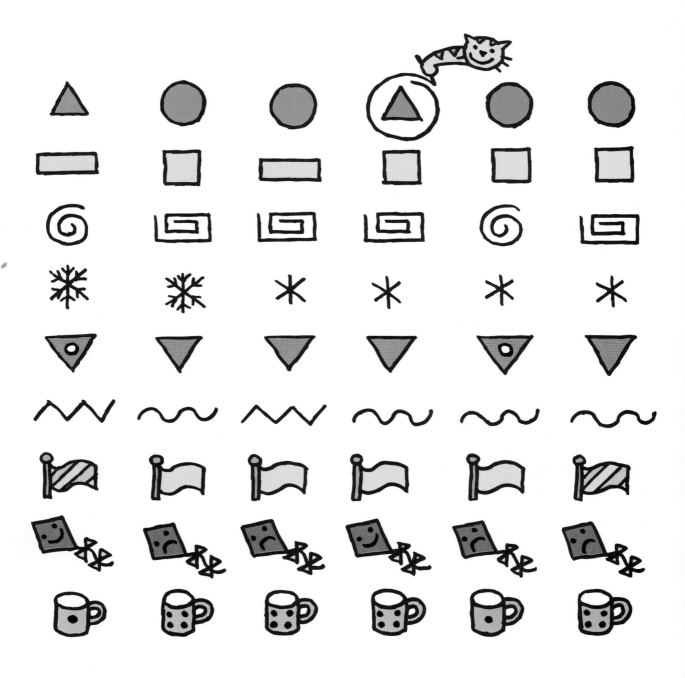

Note for parents: Some children lack confidence and ask for help when they don't really need it. Try gently encouraging your child to do it on her/his own.

Words have spaces to keep them apart.
Can you read these words?

My   name   is   Curly   Cat.

Draw a circle round each word.
Can you count them?

Ask a grown-up to help you write your name here.

My   name   is   _____

Circle and count each word.
Which word is longest?

Note for parents: Children can't learn to read until they can see words as separate units, this takes practice. When reading to your child, point to individual words.

Words can only go one way. If they go the wrong way we can't read them.

 This star shows which side words start. Start at the star.

Your name must go the right way too.
Ask a grown-up to help you write your name here.

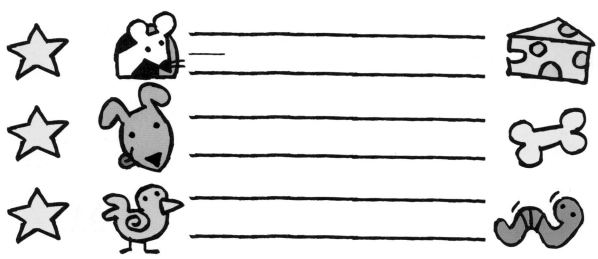

Let's practise going the right way.
Follow these paths with your
finger first, then do it
with a pencil.

Let's practise drawing lines that go the same way as words.

Help these animals find their food.

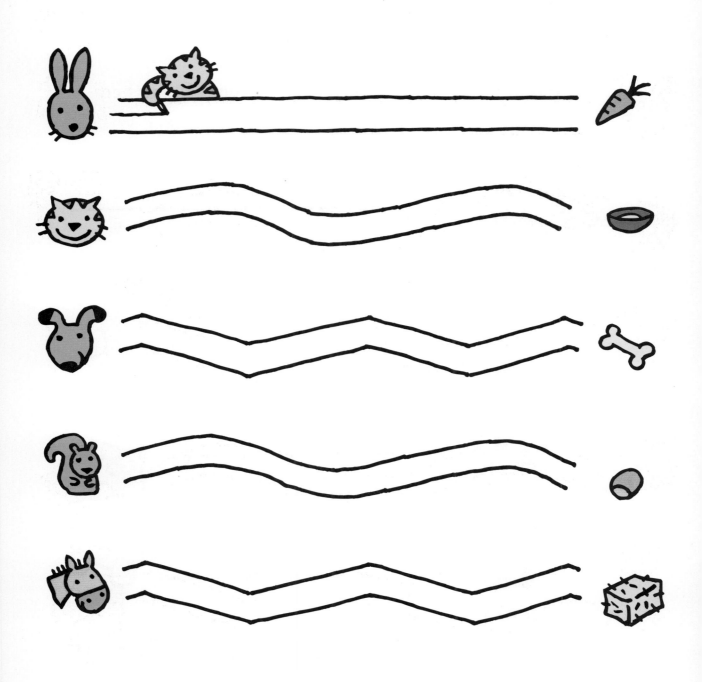

Let's practise some more.
Help these animals find their homes.

This page lets you match pictures AND draw a line the right way.

Join each picture on the left with the same one on the right. You can colour the pictures in if you like.

Good work!

Let's practise some more.
You can colour in the shoes if you like.

These pictures are like stories.
On the left are things which happen first.
Join each one across to the thing which happens next.

Note for parents: Talk about this exercise and ask your child about other sequences during the day: e.g. which comes first, breakfast or lunch?

Now let's look at real letters.
Letters are the little bits that make words.
Each one has a special shape.

Look at these letter shapes and join the ones that are the same.

Really good work!

Note for parents: At this stage, your child doesn't need to know what sound the letters make. On this page, we are using only letters with obvious similarities and differences.

Here are some more letters to match.
Look carefully at the shapes.

o   e   i   r

d   r   o

e   i   d

And here are some more:

e   s   p   t

t   p   y

s   y   e

Let's do one more page like that.
Are you holding your pencil properly?

n   e   h

s   o   n   p

e   p

h   o   s

Here are the letters which make the word **cat**

Look at the letters below and put a circle round
the ones which you can see in cat.

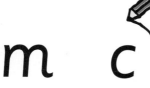

m   c   s   a   p   i   t

You are good at matching letters.

Here are some more letters.
Join each one on the left to the same one on the right.
Put a star on the side of the page where you start.

⭐ a ... s

i ... a

s ... p

e ... h

p ... i

h ... e

Fantastic matching work!

Let's do some more just like that.

You'll need to look extra carefully at these letters.
Some of them look nearly the same.

a o e

i c

o e i

c a

Note for parents: These letters are slightly harder for your child to match because they all have a similar shape. The next pages look more closely at differences between letters.

Do the same here. Look very carefully.

Choose a gold star!

Note for parents: Make a double set of alphabet cards. Select just the letters we have been using so far and ask your child to find pairs.

Here's something new.
Some of these things point different ways.
Look at the picture on the left (the star side).
Then look along the line and circle one that points the same
way. They must be the same way up too.

Note for parents: Reinforce this idea with real objects: use cutlery, toy animals, pencils, etc. Lay one in one direction and ask your child arrange the others to face the same way.

Let's do some more like that.

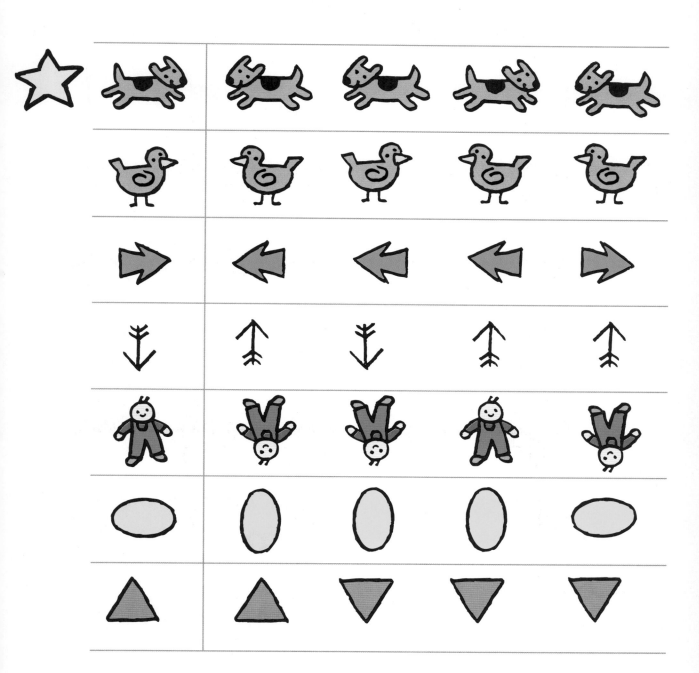

Note for parents: The next pages work on letters which are mirror images of other letters. Your child needs to be confident with the letters learned so far before moving on in the book.

Look very carefully at these tricky letters.
Join the same ones with a line.
Remember, they have to point the same way.

n   d

u   p   d

p   u   n

Very well done! Now try some more.

w   q   b

                                m

b   m   w   q

Let's do some more like that.

That was good.

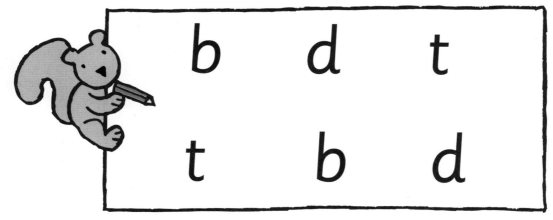

b	d	t
t	b	d

And one more time:

p	q	b	u
u	n	p	
q	b	n	

Here's something new.
Do you know about odd one out?
The odd one out is the one that's different from all the others.

Circle the odd one out inside each sack.

That was clever. Can you do some more?

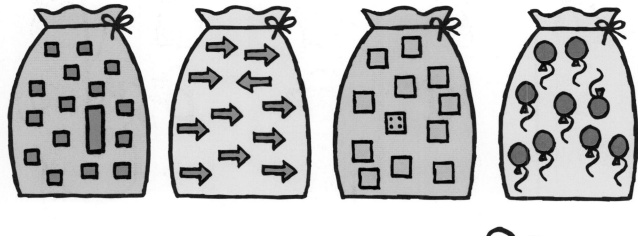

Note for parents: This is another way of looking for differences. Practise with physical objects, choosing groups where all but one are exactly the same, e.g. 5 red bricks and 1 blue brick.

Let's practise odd one out.
Look along each line and circle the odd one out.

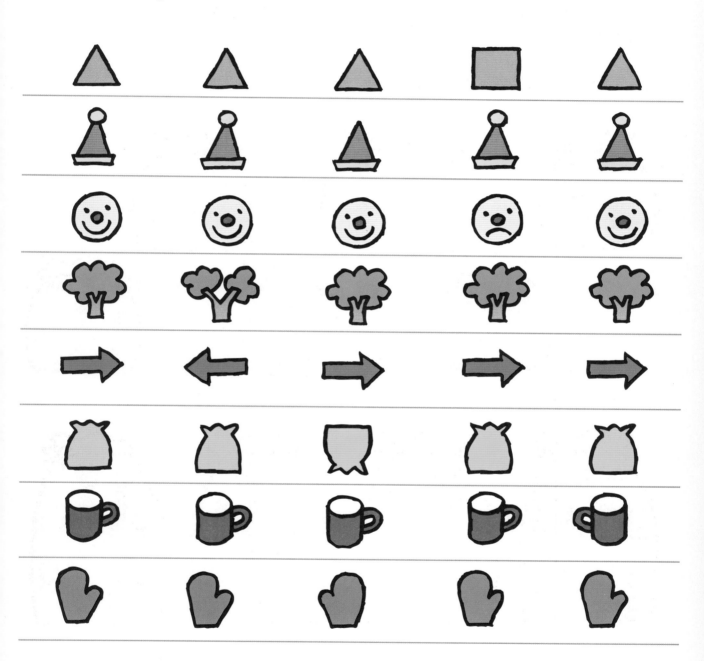

Some children made sandcastles and put a flag on top.
But the wind blew the flags away.
Can you find the right flag for each sandcastle?

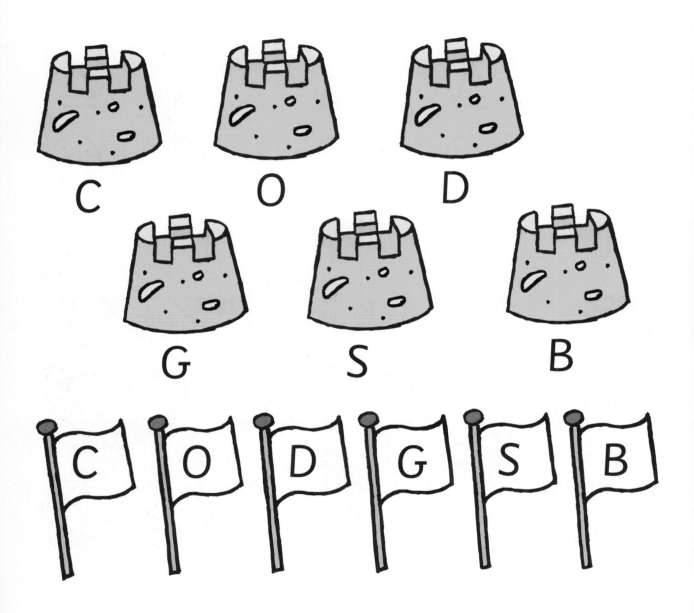

I need some help again.
It's Christmas and my kittens each have two presents.
But which are the right ones? Can you join the presents
to the right kittens?

Let's do something with a very special word – your name.

Ask a grown-up to help you write your name on the line below.

_____

Now look at the alphabet.
Join each letter in your name to the same one in the alphabet.

a b c d e f g h i
j k l m n o p q r
s t u v w x y z

Did you find them all? Choose a big gold star!

Note for parents: Write your child's name on a piece of paper and cut it into letters. Can s/he put the letters in the right order? Children love to write their own name.

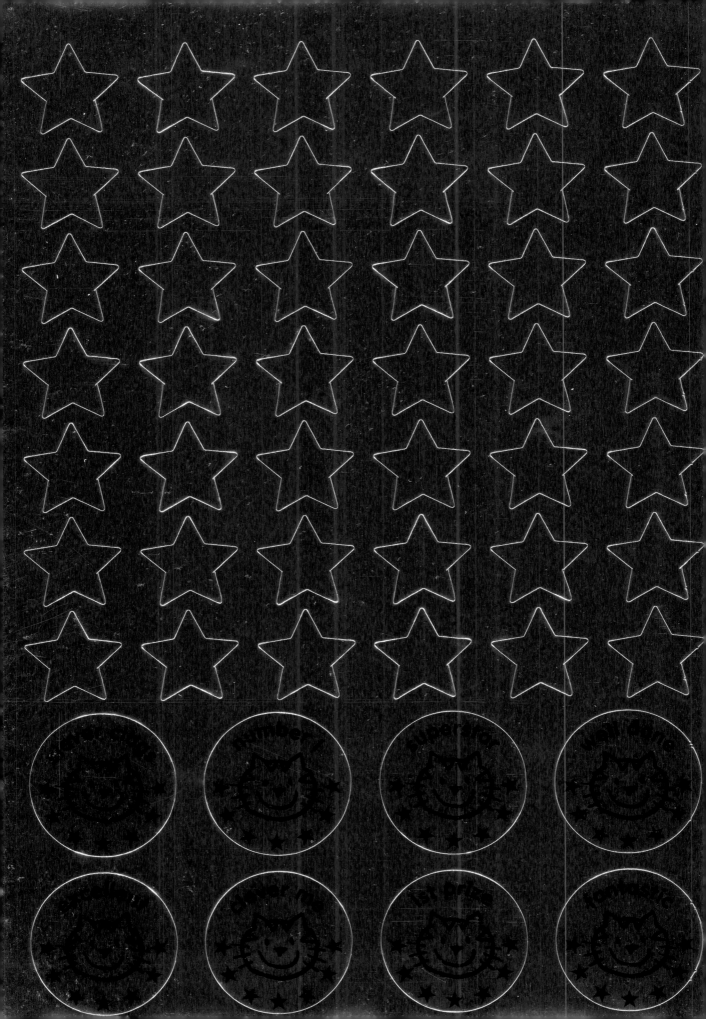